COLOURING AND ACTIVITY BOOK

marvelkids.com

© 2018 MARVEL

Autumn Publishing

D0192363

THOR

CONNECT THE DOTS

Iron Man is battling one of the Avengers' most dangerous enemies. Connect the dots to find out who.

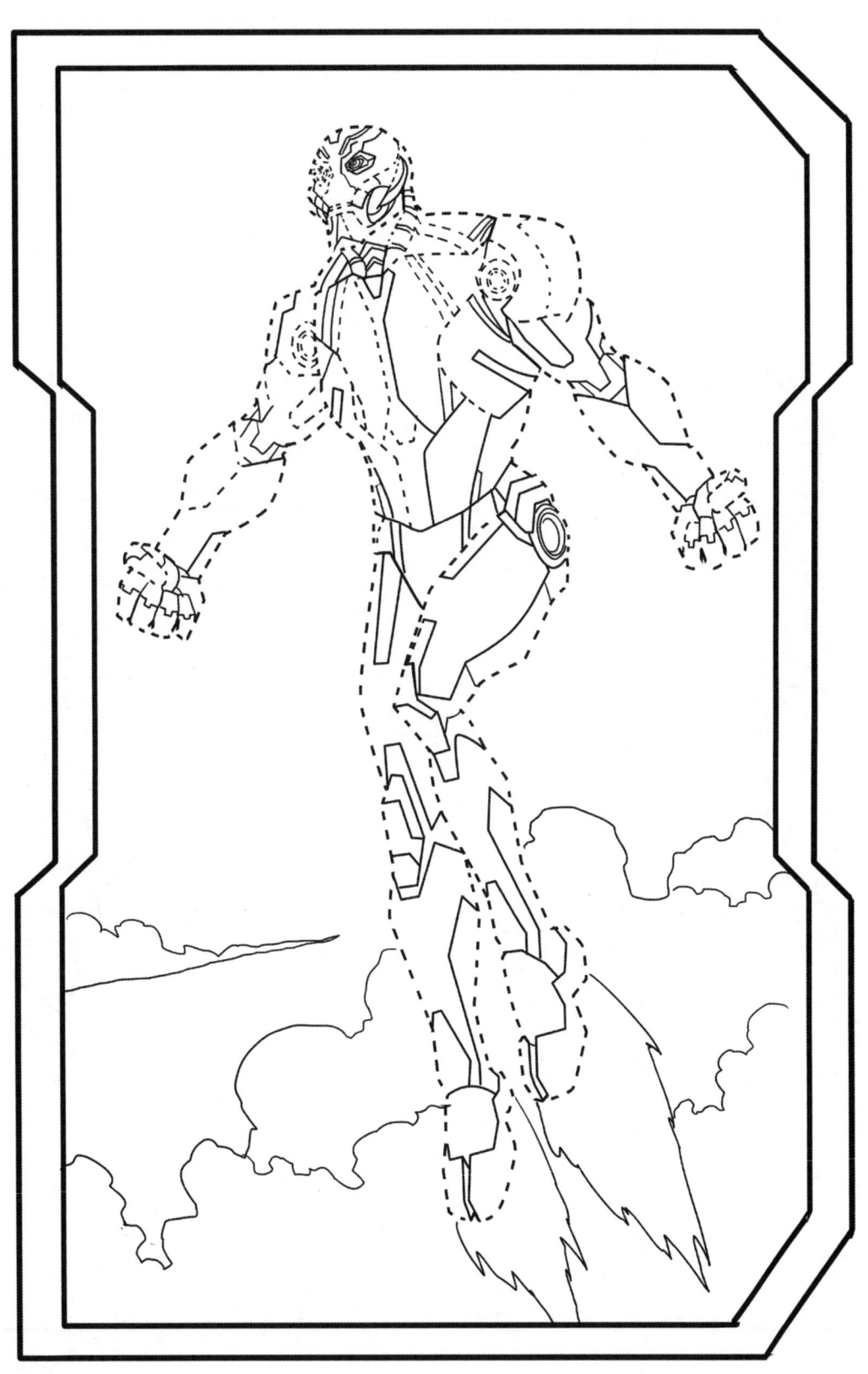

IMAGE SEARCH

Tony Stark has created hundreds of Iron Man suits to help the Avengers. How many can you find in this picture?

"HULK ASSEMBLE... THEN SMASH!"

THOR

"Never fear, Asgard's MIGHTY Avenger is here!"

DRAWING

Captain America is missing something very important.
Can you figure out what it is, then draw it in?

FILL IN THE BLANKS

The Avengers were first assembled by the director of S.H.I.E.L.D.. Can you fill in the blanks below to complete his name?

N___ K F_R__

"Better not lose control, HULK.
I'm keeping an eye on you."

CROSSWORD

Fill in the crossword using the clues below.

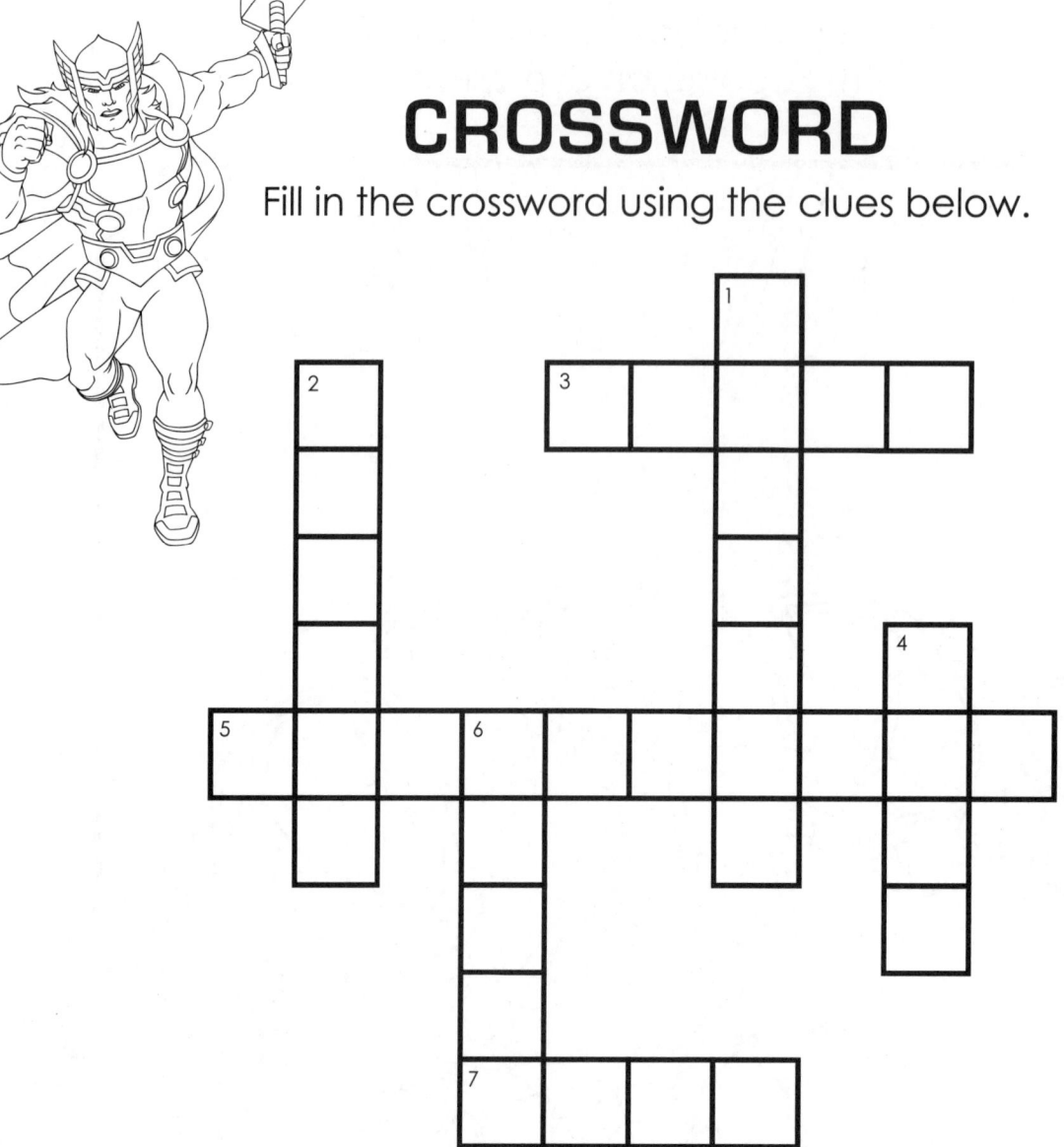

Across:

3. What is Iron Man's last name in real life?
5. Natasha Romanoff is also known as _____.
7. Which Avenger can control lightning and thunder?

Down:

1. What military rank does Steve Rogers go by?
2. What is the name of the organisation headed by Nick Fury?
4. What is the name of Thor's mischievous brother?
6. What is Hawkeye's first name in real life?

HAWKEYE: "I can hit any target from a mile away."
BLACK WIDOW: "Who needs arrows? I have fists."

MAZE

Thor needs to take the Bifröst Bridge from Asgard to Earth.
Help Heimdall find the right path to get Thor there.

Start

Finish

Answer in Back of Book.

DRAWING

Falcon is missing one of his wings.
Use the grid below to fill it in.

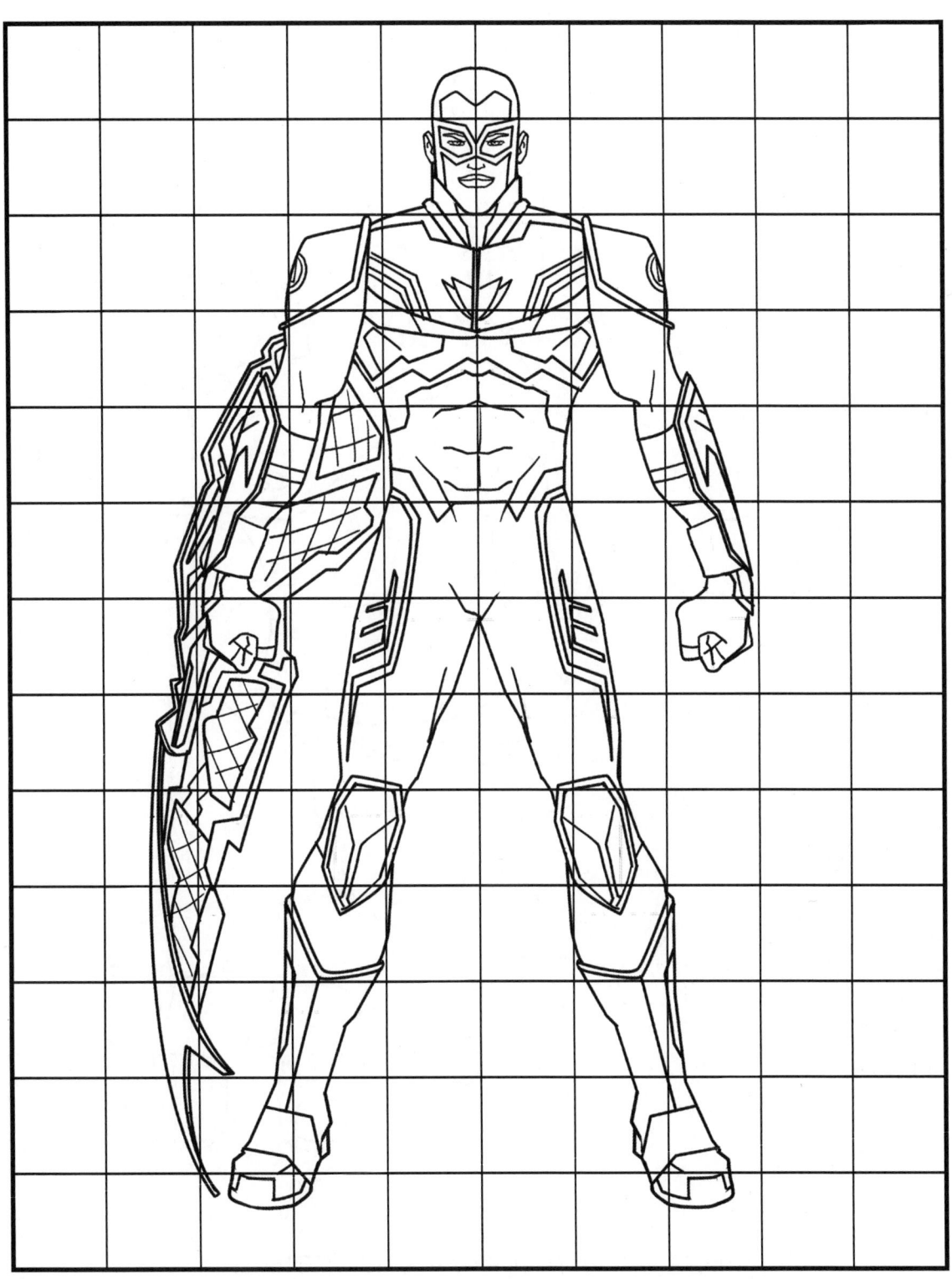

Hulk is the strongest one there is!

Gamma Ray Radiation

WORD SEARCH

Time to assemble! How many of these
Avengers' names can you find?

```
Q W E R T Y U I
G H A W K E Y E
T U G A H A X F
I H A F U H J A
O Z O C L B N L
T P O R K Y G C
R D R X W Q A O
L K A J H G F N
```

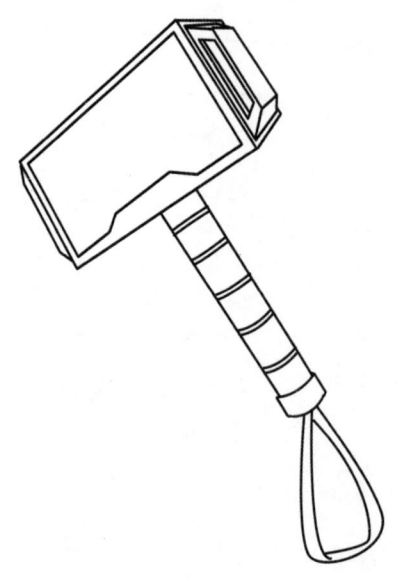

★ ★ ★

THOR

FALCON

HULK

HAWKEYE

★ ★ ★

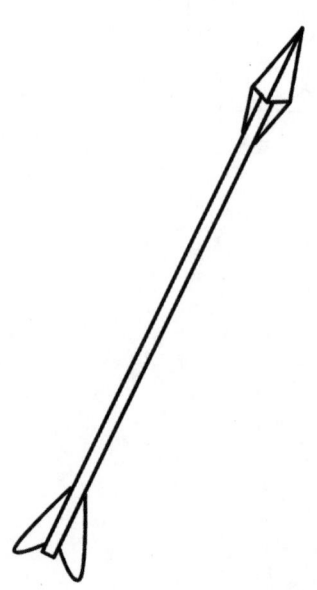

Answer in Back of Book.

ANAGRAM

The Super Villain Ultron was created by using what?
Unscramble the letters below to find out.

R A I T I F I C L A

N I E T L L G I N E E C

CONNECT THE DOTS

Connect the dots to see who must give the
order for the Avengers to assemble.

Loki leaves Asgard to cause mischief on Earth.

SPOT THE DIFFERENCE

Can you spot the five differences
between these two pictures of Hulk?

MAZE

Help Black Widow infiltrate
Hydra Headquarters.

Finish

Start

The Chitauri want to take over Earth.

Attuma is a great conqueror.

DRAWING BY HALVES

Draw Iron Man's other half,
using the grid to help you.

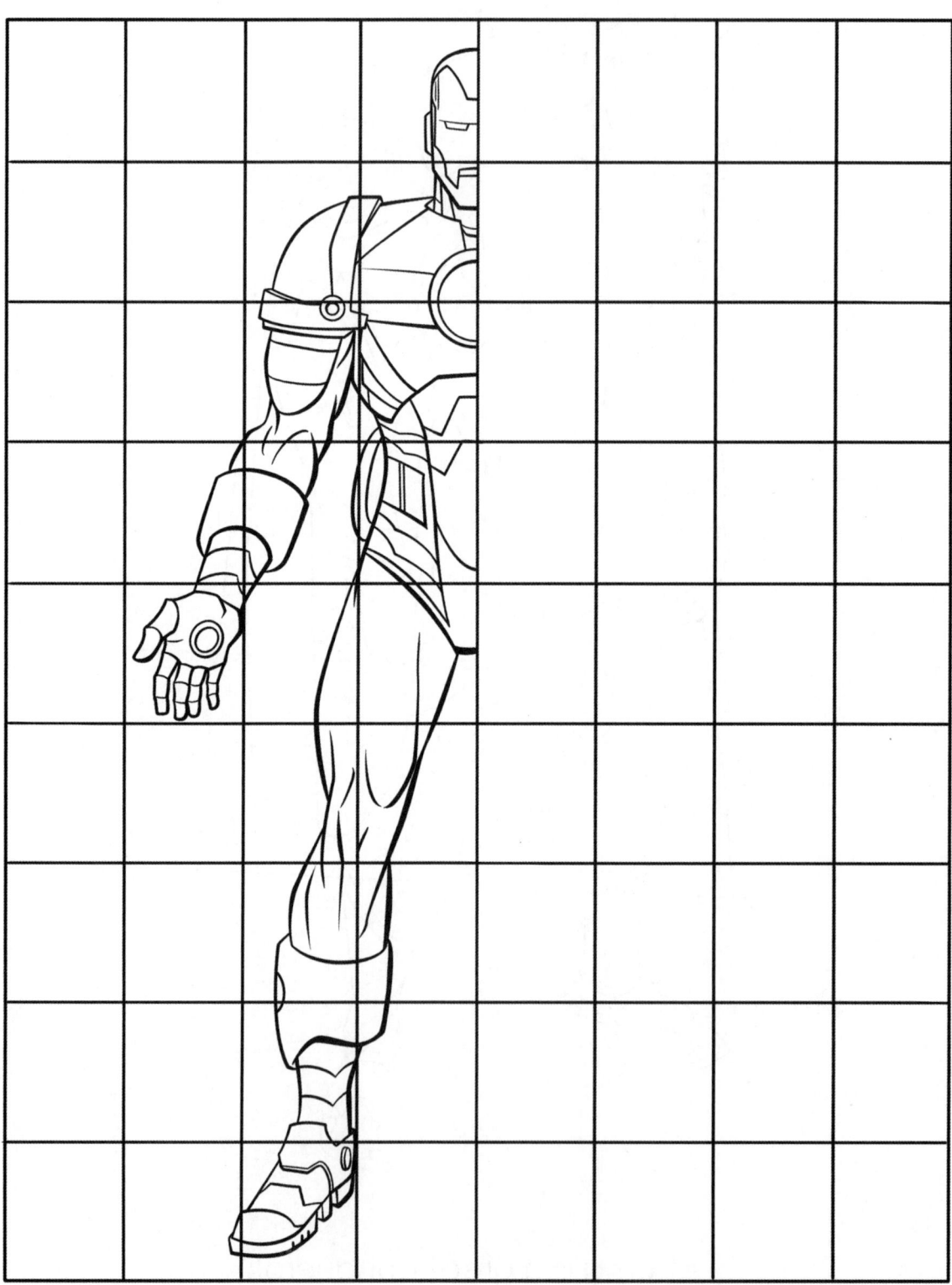

RED HULK, GREEN HULK, 1, 2, 3

We all know Hulk with his familiar green skin. But what would he look like in other colours? Try it out and see!

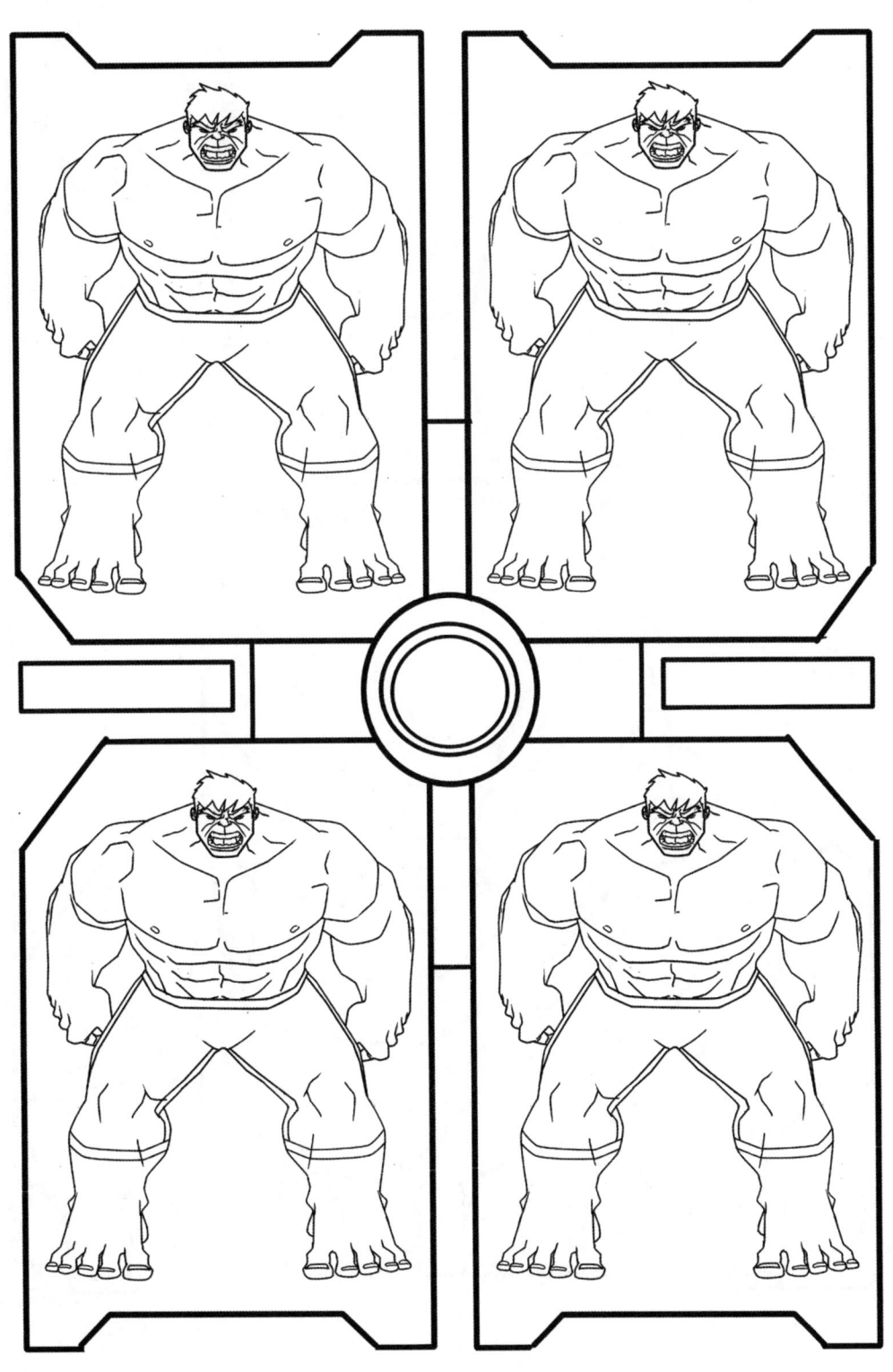

DRAWING

Finish drawing Captain America's shield, then show what your shield would look like if you were one of the Avengers.

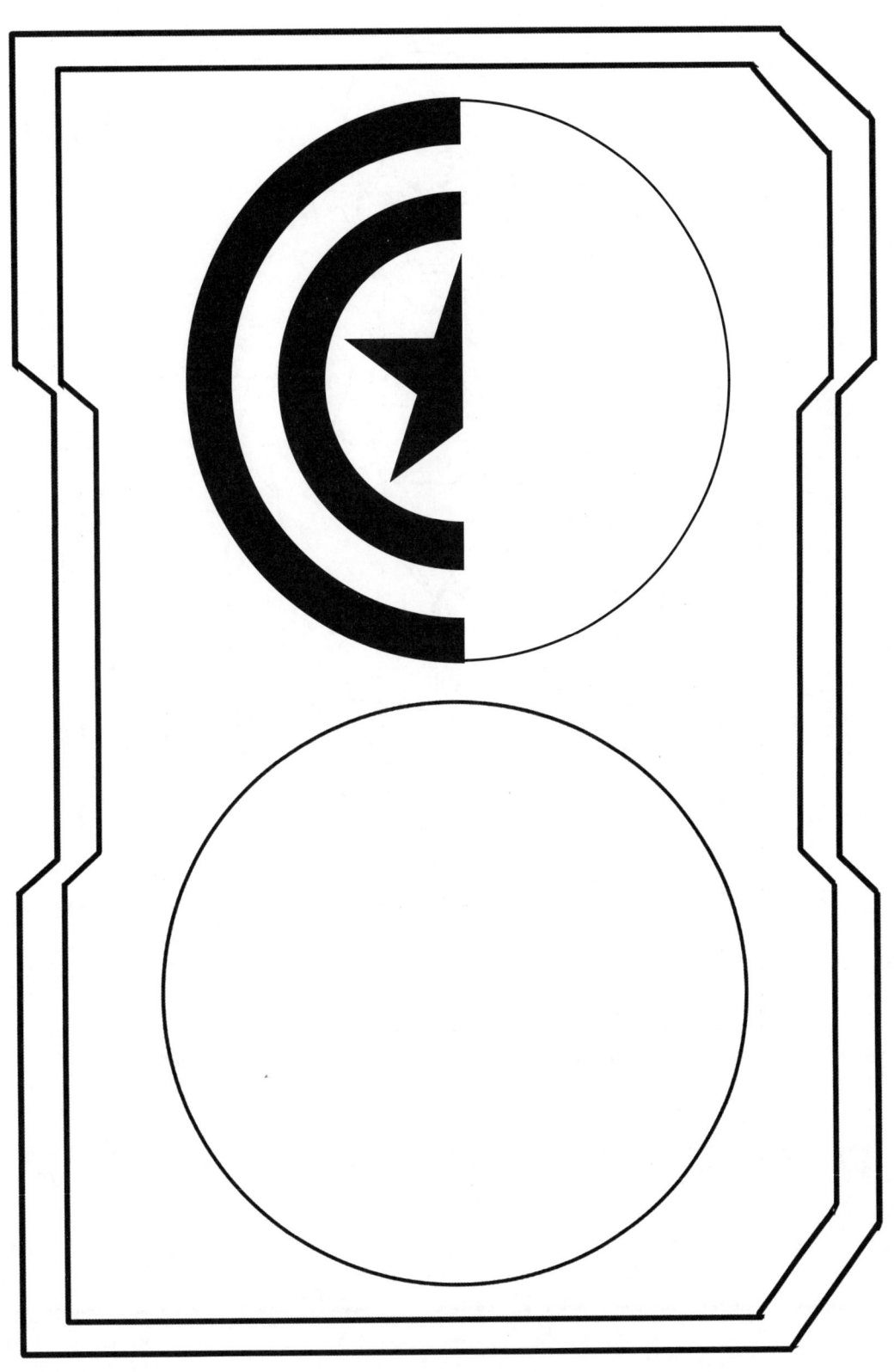

ANAGRAM

Unscramble the letters to spell the
name of Tony Stark's secretary.

P P R E P E   S T O T P

_ _ _ _ _ _   _ _ _ _ _

RIDDLE

What gave Steve Rogers the increased stamina,
speed and strength he has as Captain America?
Cross out all the *V*s and *G*s to answer the riddle.

VGSUVPGGEVR   SVGVOVLDVIGEVRG
GSEVGRVUGGVMV

IDENTIFYING

Which one of these is Captain America's mask?

A

B

C

D

DRAWING

What if the Super Heroes in the Avengers could
mix and match their powers? Draw what a hero would
look like if he or she had multiple Avenger powers.

CODE BREAKING

Break the code to discover Black Widow's
real name. Replace each letter below with the
letter that comes before it in the alphabet.

O B U B T I B

S P N B O P G G

_____

_____

NICK FURY

SPOT THE DIFFERENCE

One of these Iron Man suits is a fake.
Can you figure out which?

A   B

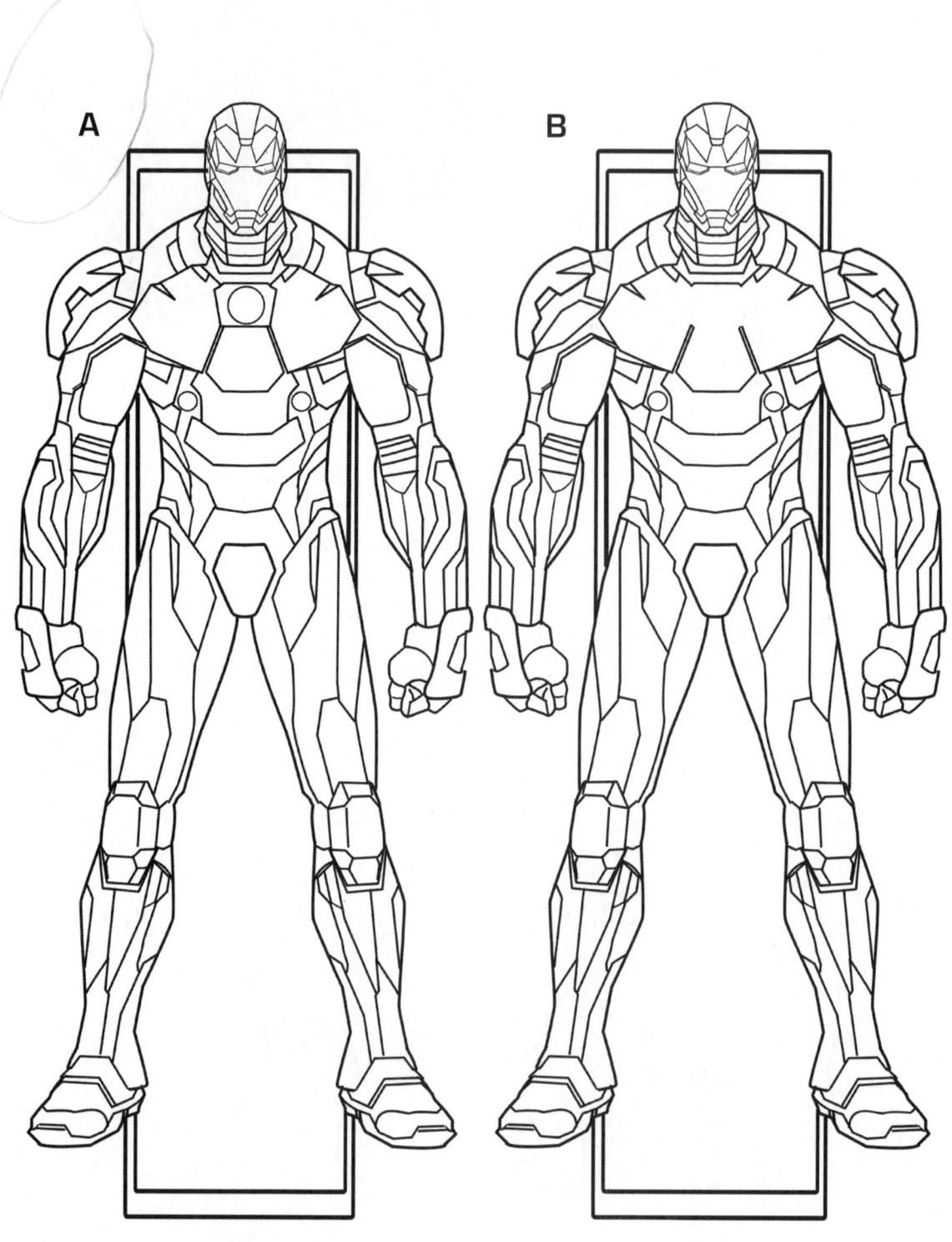

CAPTAIN AMERICA

RIDDLE

What is the name of Tony Stark's computer assistant?
Cross out every other letter to answer the riddle.

J I A K R P V I I B S X

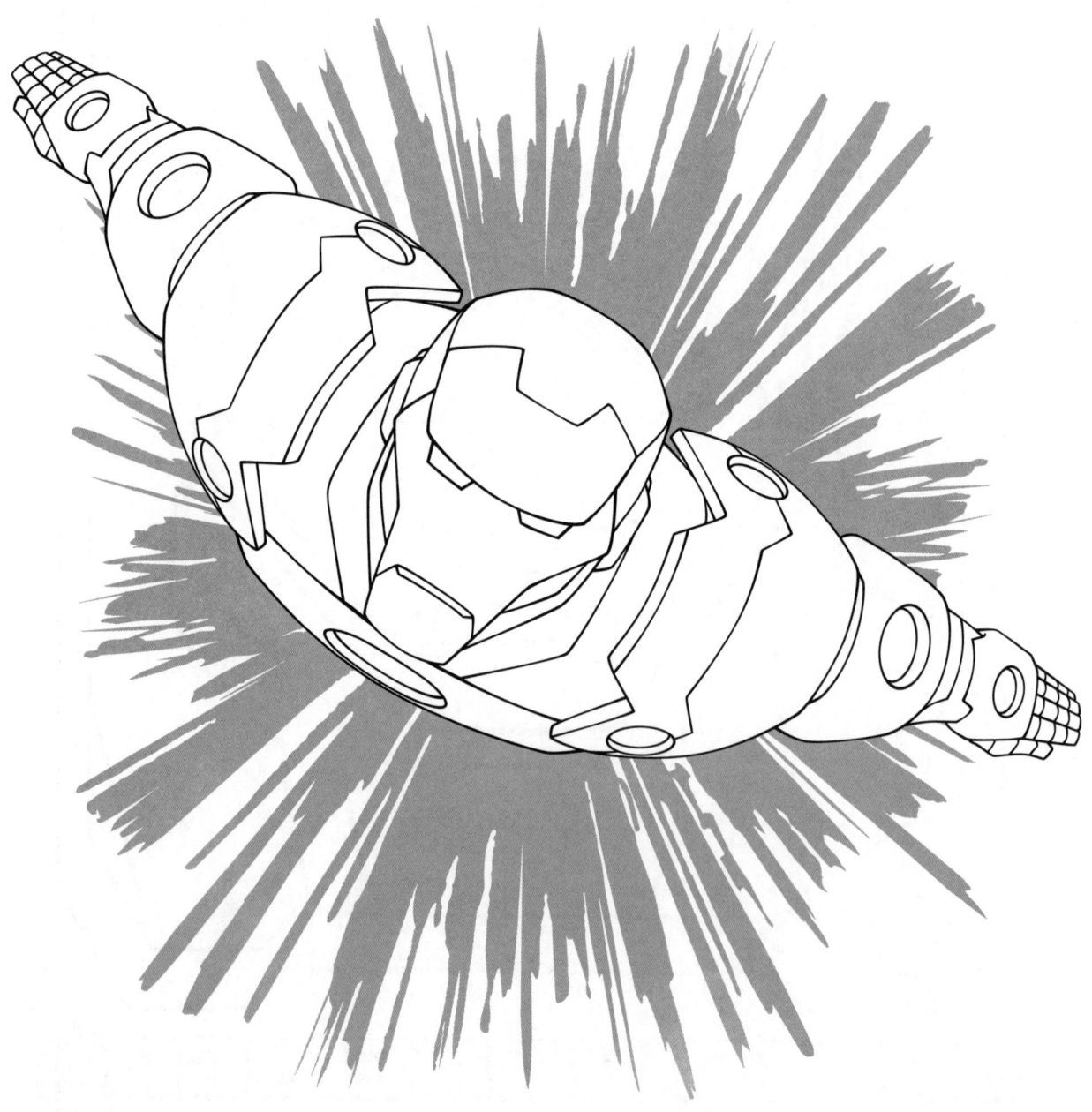

MAZE

Nick Fury needs to assemble the Avengers team.
Help each Avenger find the best path to the middle.

MISSING PIECES

Uh-oh, this image of Thor hasn't been finished. Fill in the rest of the grid so he can join the other Avengers.

ULTRON

MATCHING

Which arrowhead does Hawkeye use?
Find the arrow below that matches.

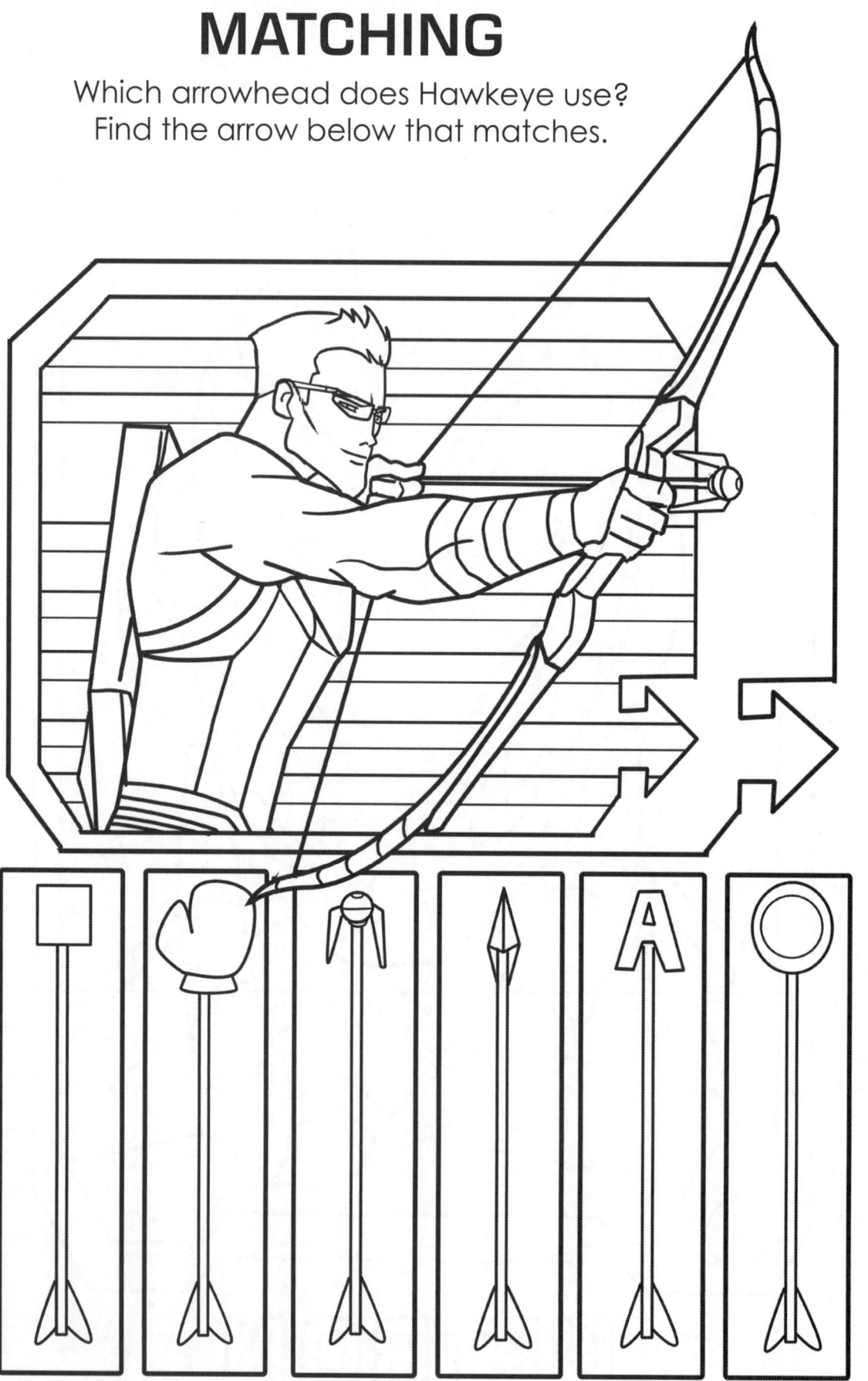

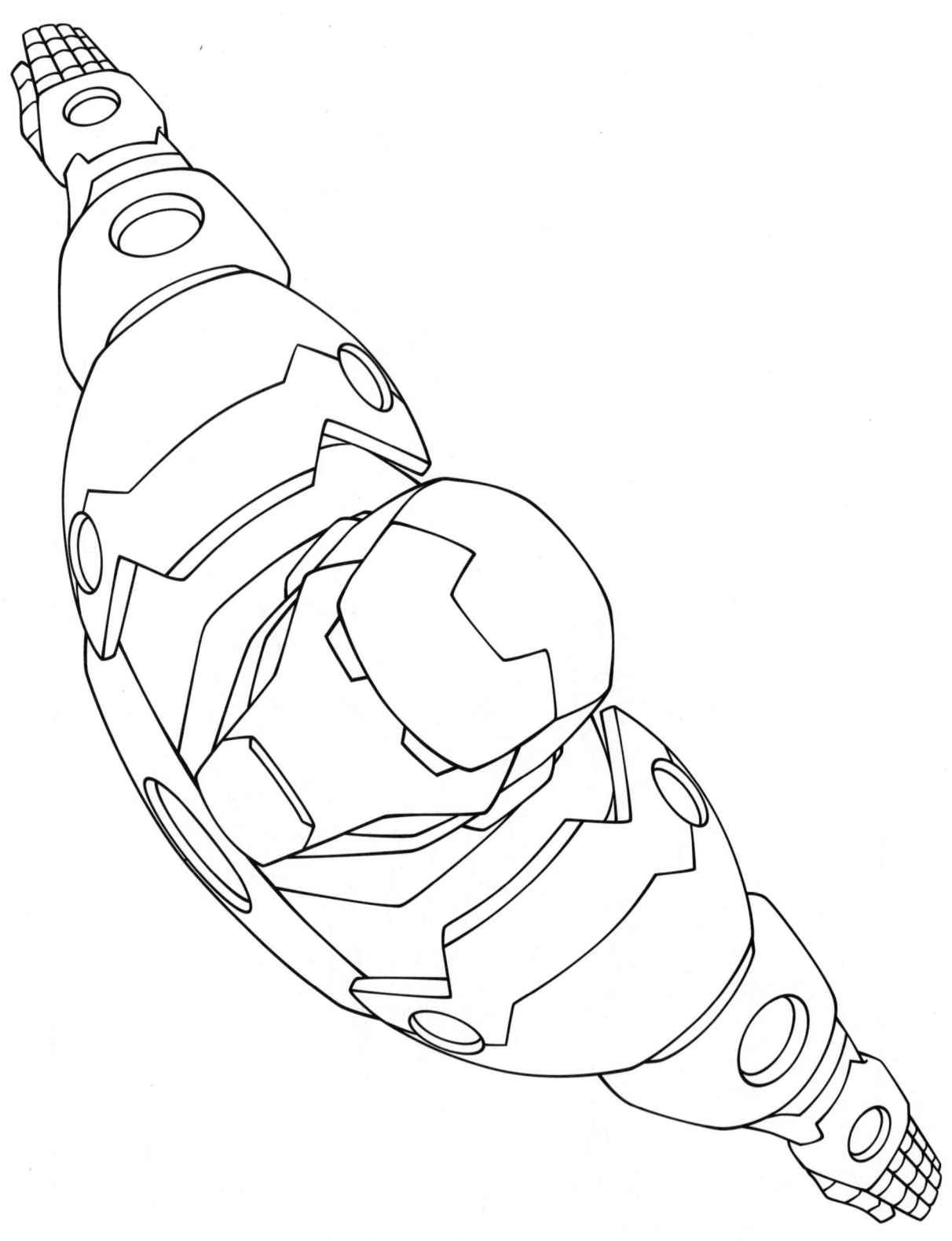

Armour up!

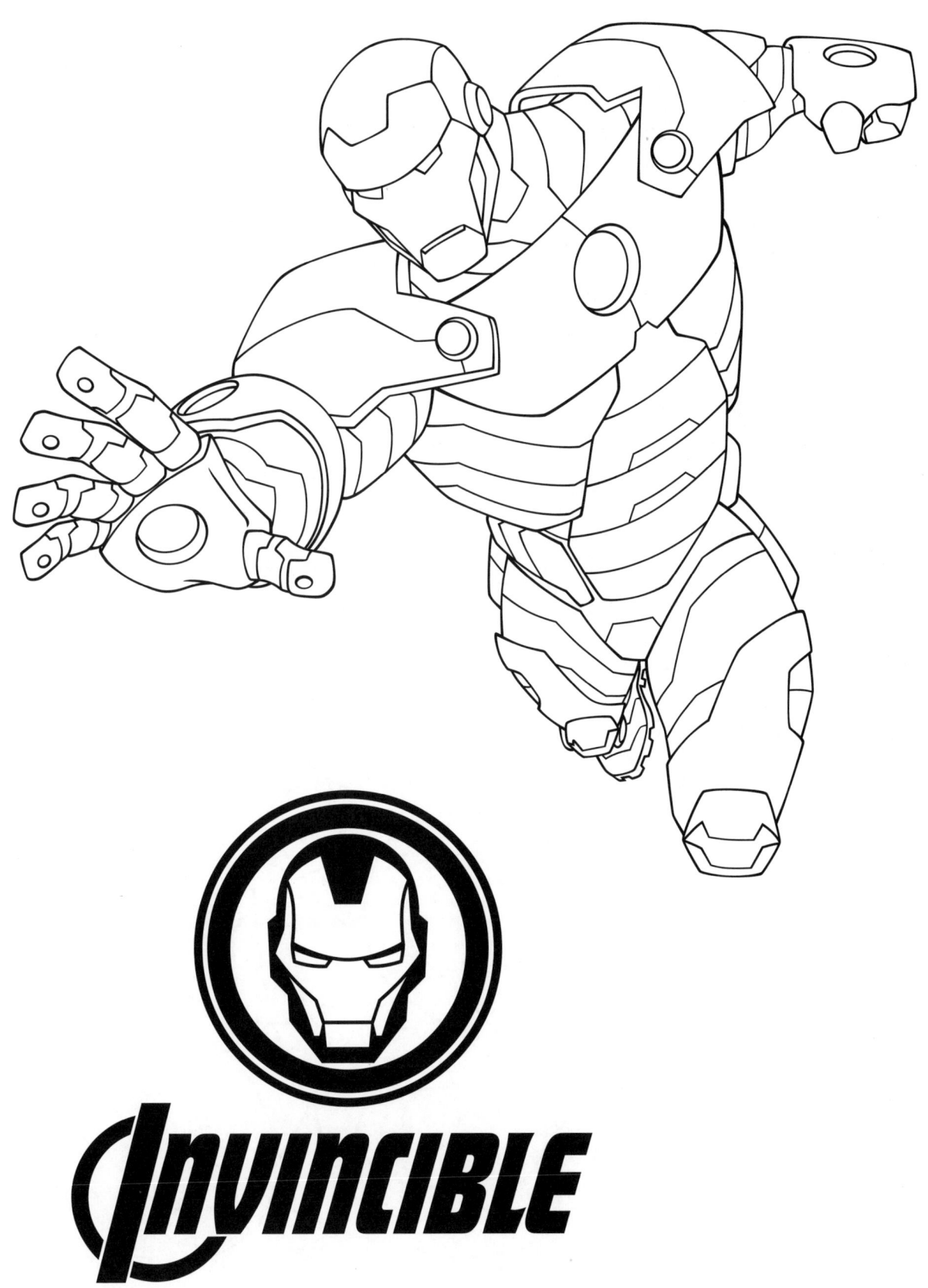

INVINCIBLE

MAZE

Help Iron Man choose the
correct path to the open door.

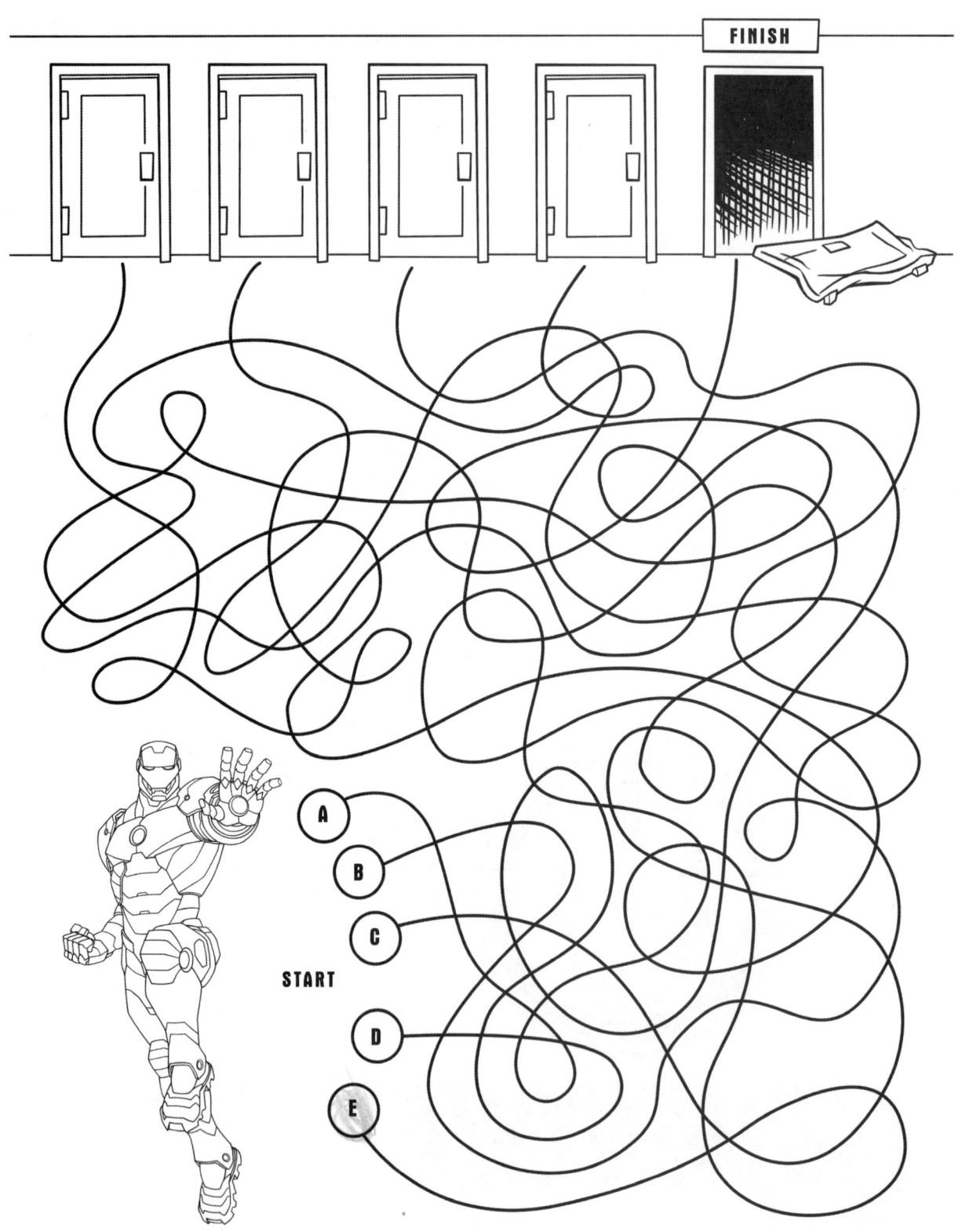

The Big Guy

"Now Hulk MAD!"

IMAGE SEARCH

Black Widow is a master spy. See if you can find her hiding somewhere in this picture.

DRAWING BY HALVES

Finish this drawing of Iron Man.

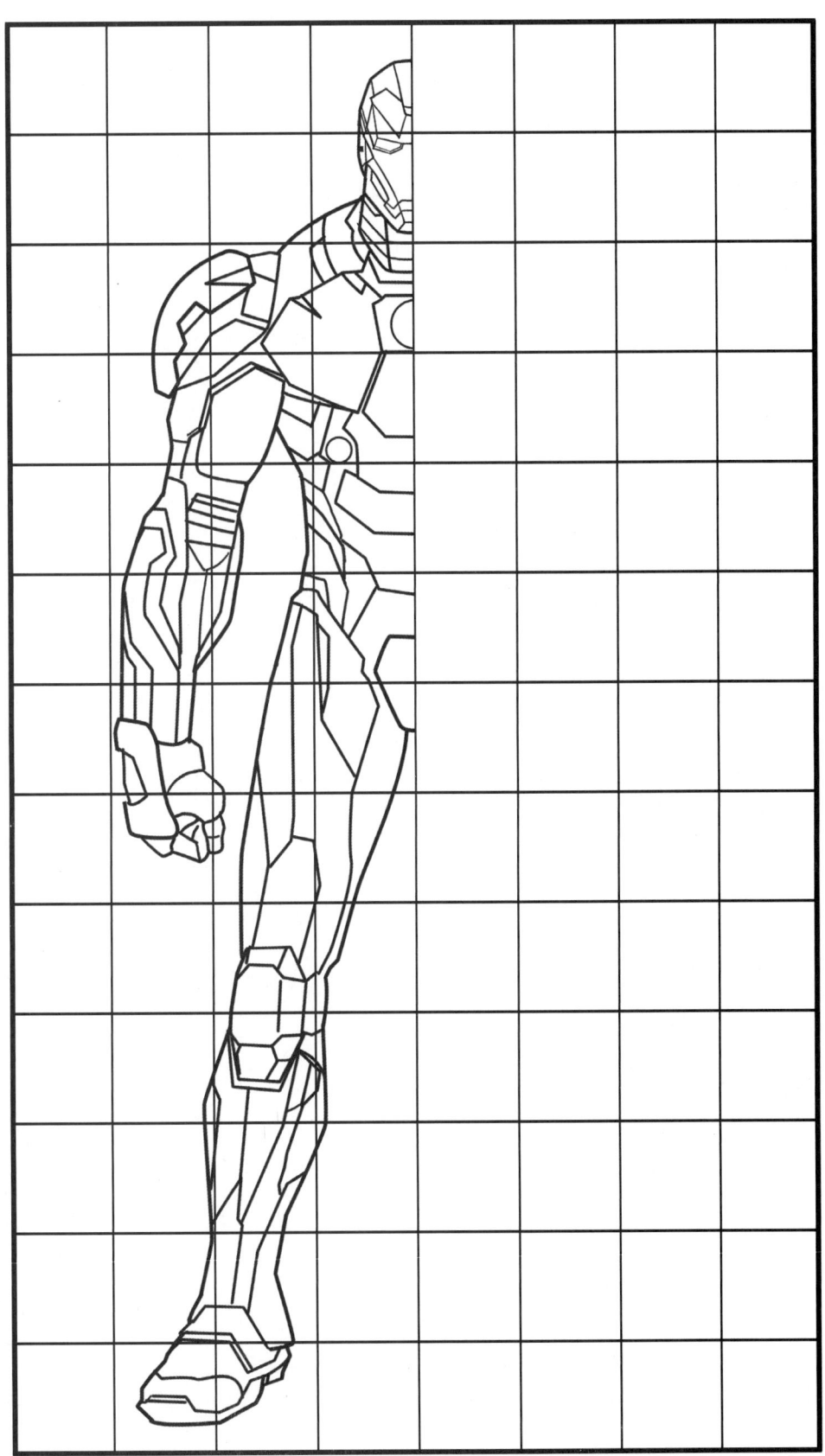

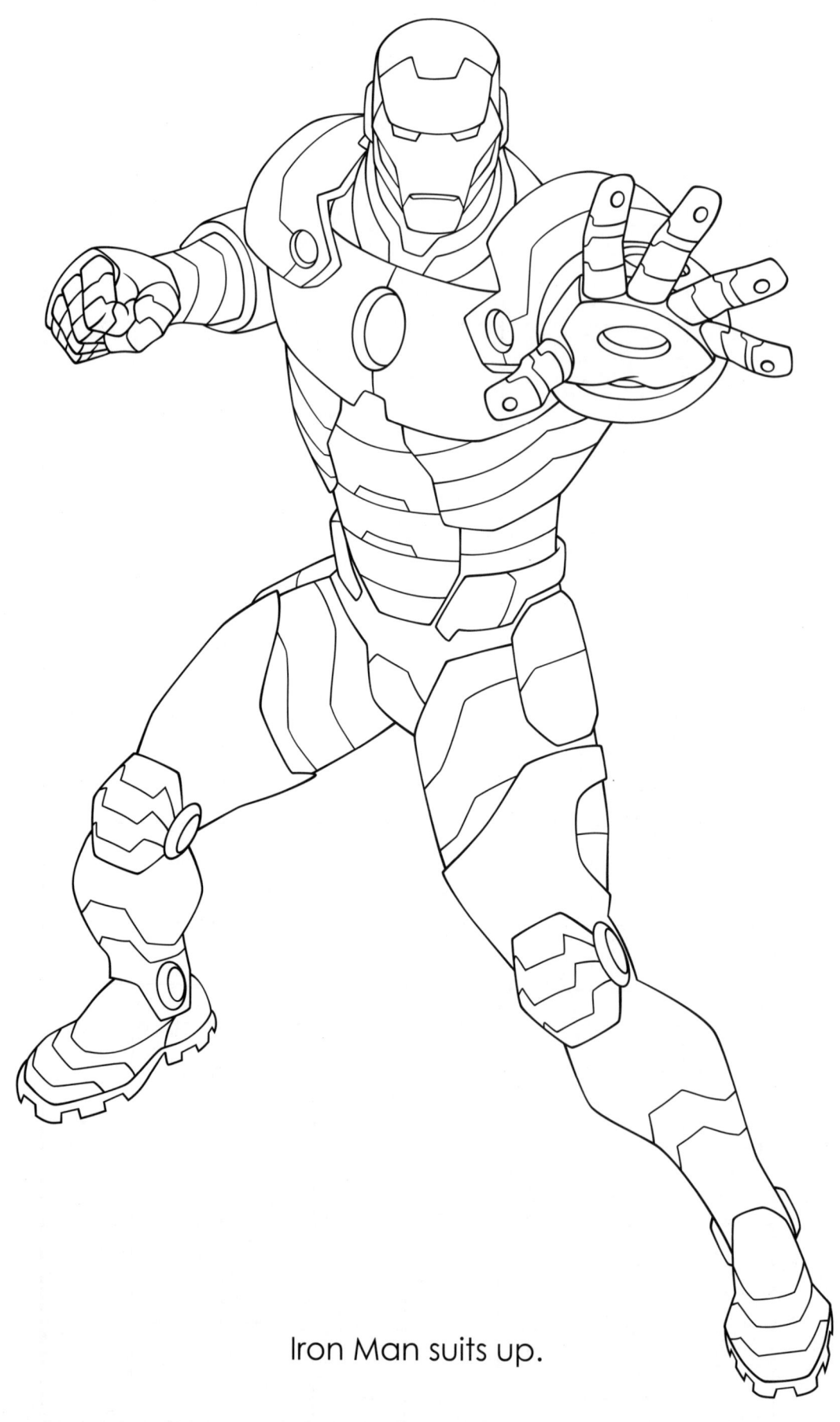

Iron Man suits up.

Using the grid
as a guide, draw
The Hulk.

DRAWING

Iron Man uses his powerful jet thrusters to fly. Draw the missing thrusters from his boots and gloves to help him stay in the air.

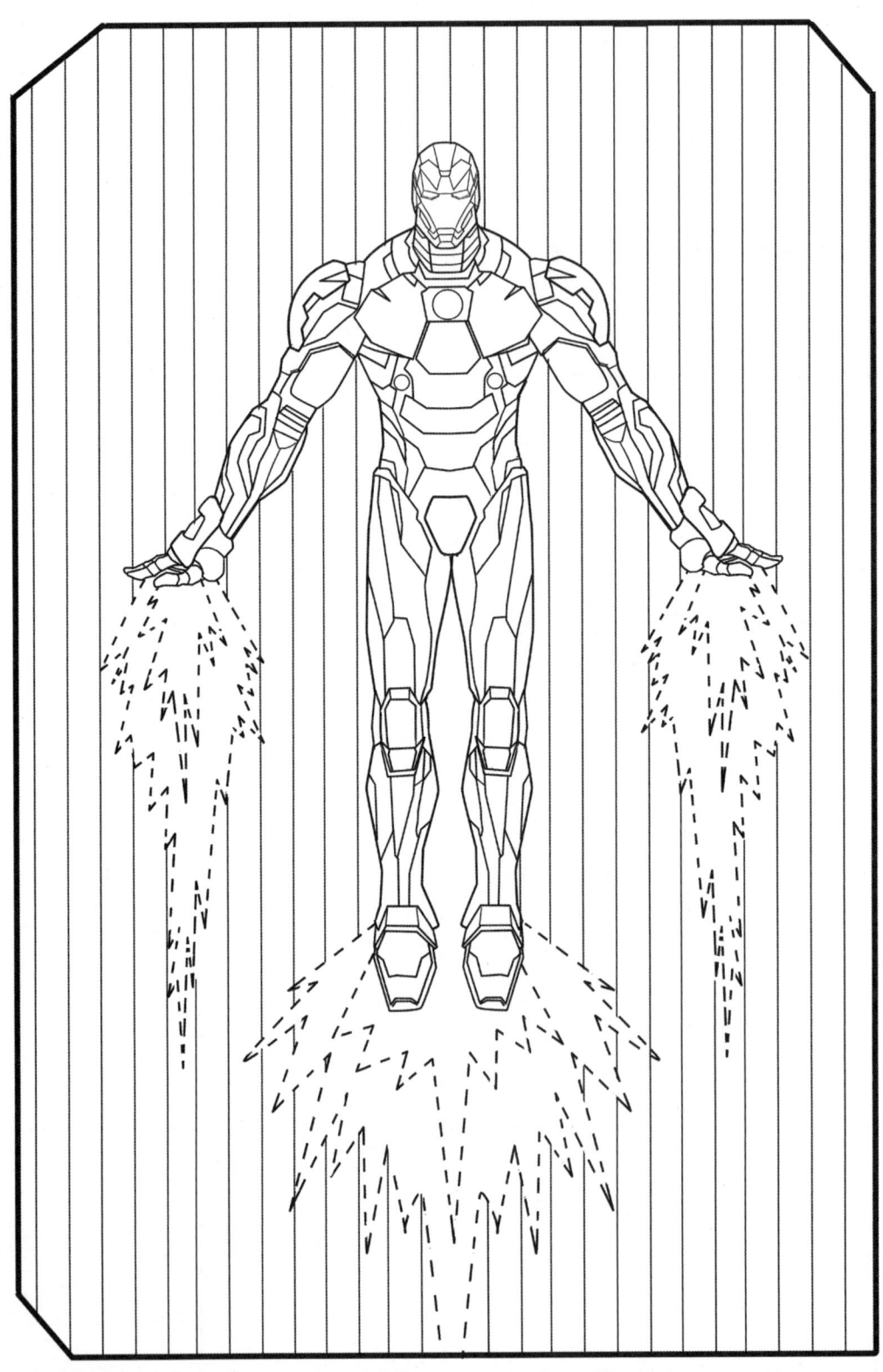

S.H.I.E.L.D. stands for Strategic Homeland Intervention,
Enforcement and Logistics Division.

How many words can you
make using the letters in:

THE
ABOMINATION

_____   _____

_____   _____

_____   _____

_____   _____

_____   _____

_____   _____

_____   _____

The Red Skull works with Hydra.

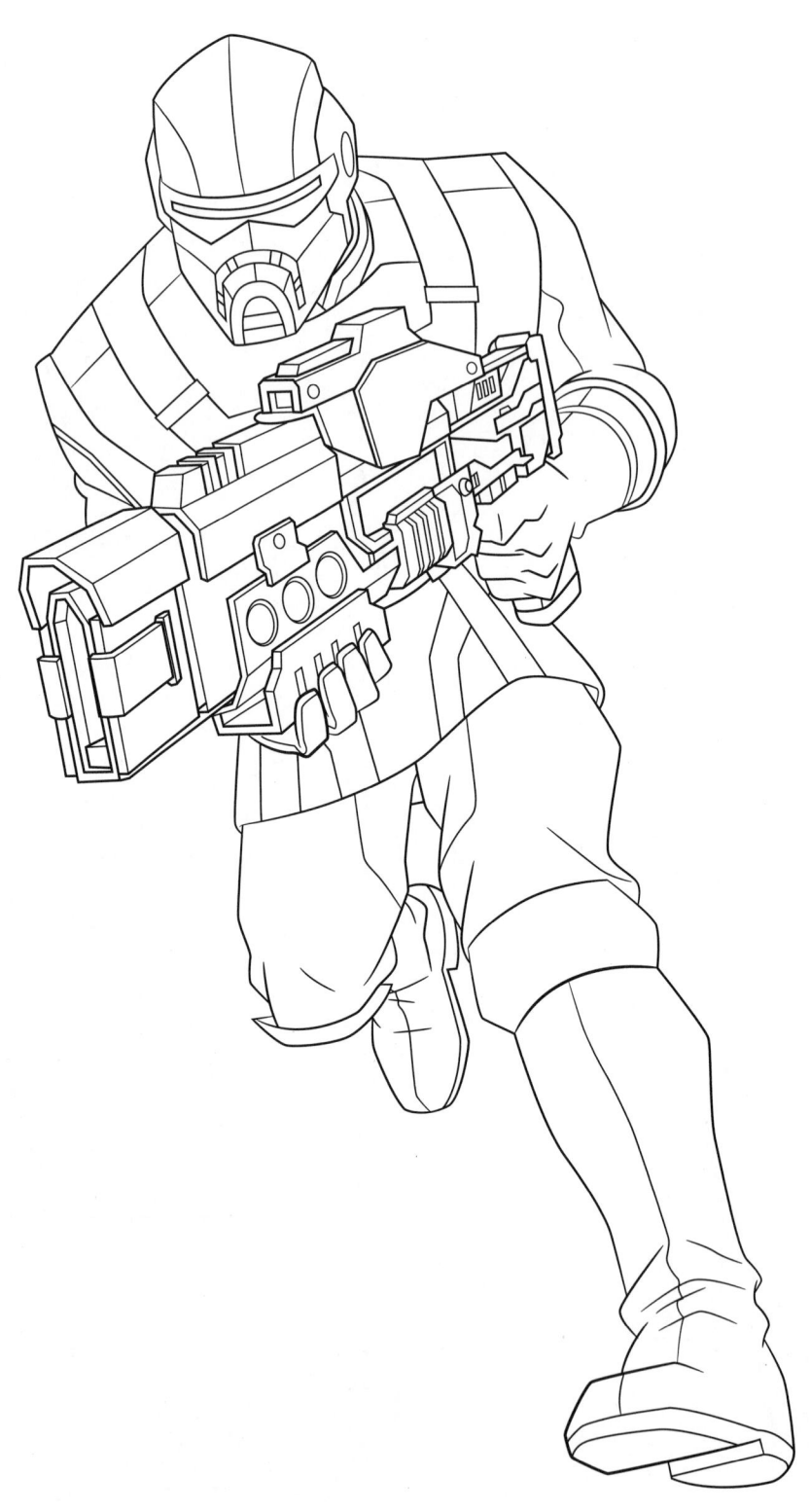

A Hydra Agent.

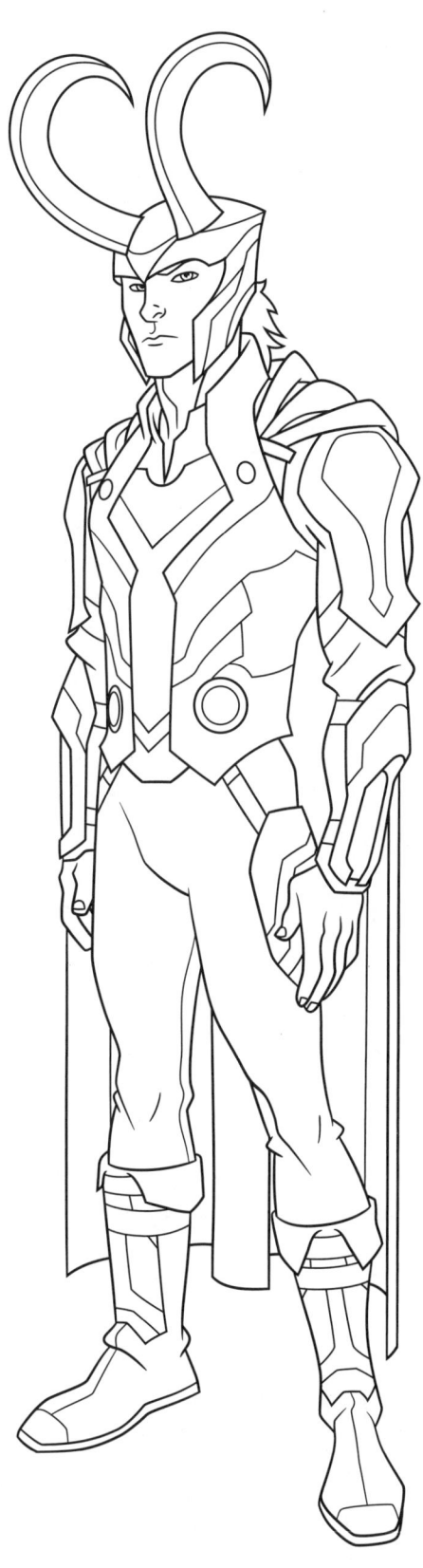

Loki is Thor's evil brother.

THE INCREDIBLE
HULK

VS

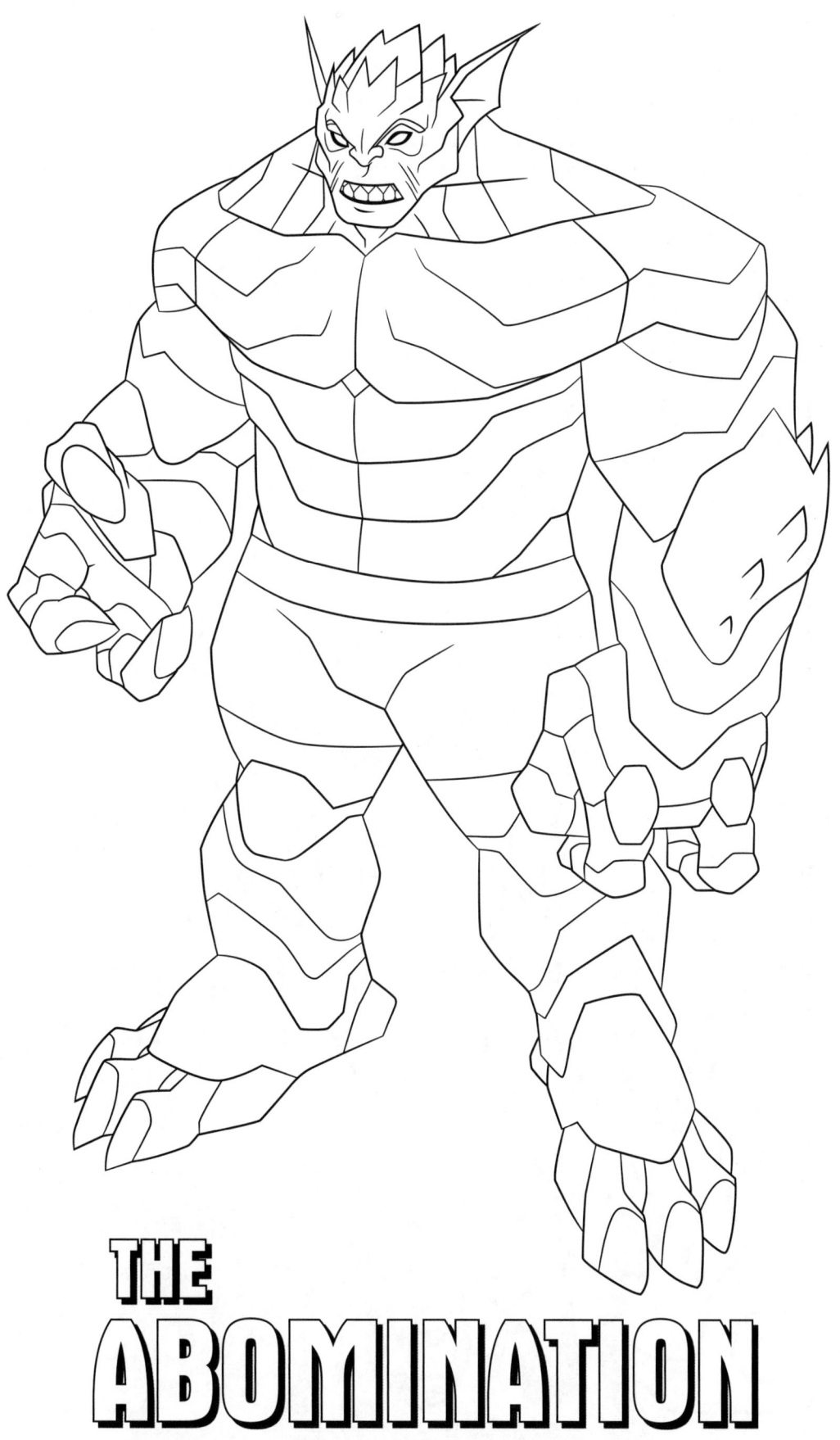

THE
ABOMINATION

MAZE

The Avengers are in their headquarters when they hear a distress call from downtown. Find the quickest way to get them there in rush hour.

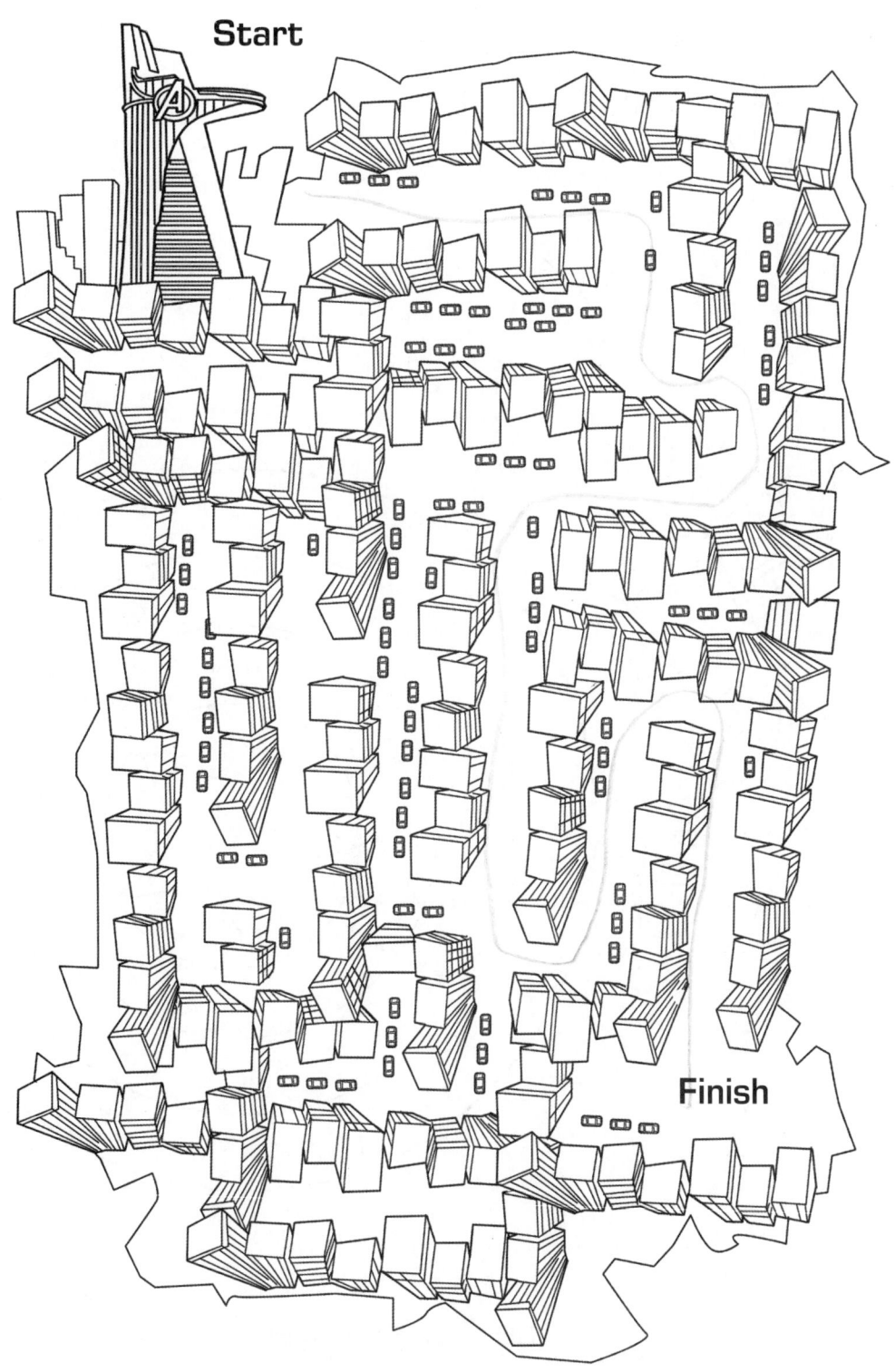

Start

Finish

The First Avenger

REAL SHIELD

Which shield belongs to Captain America?

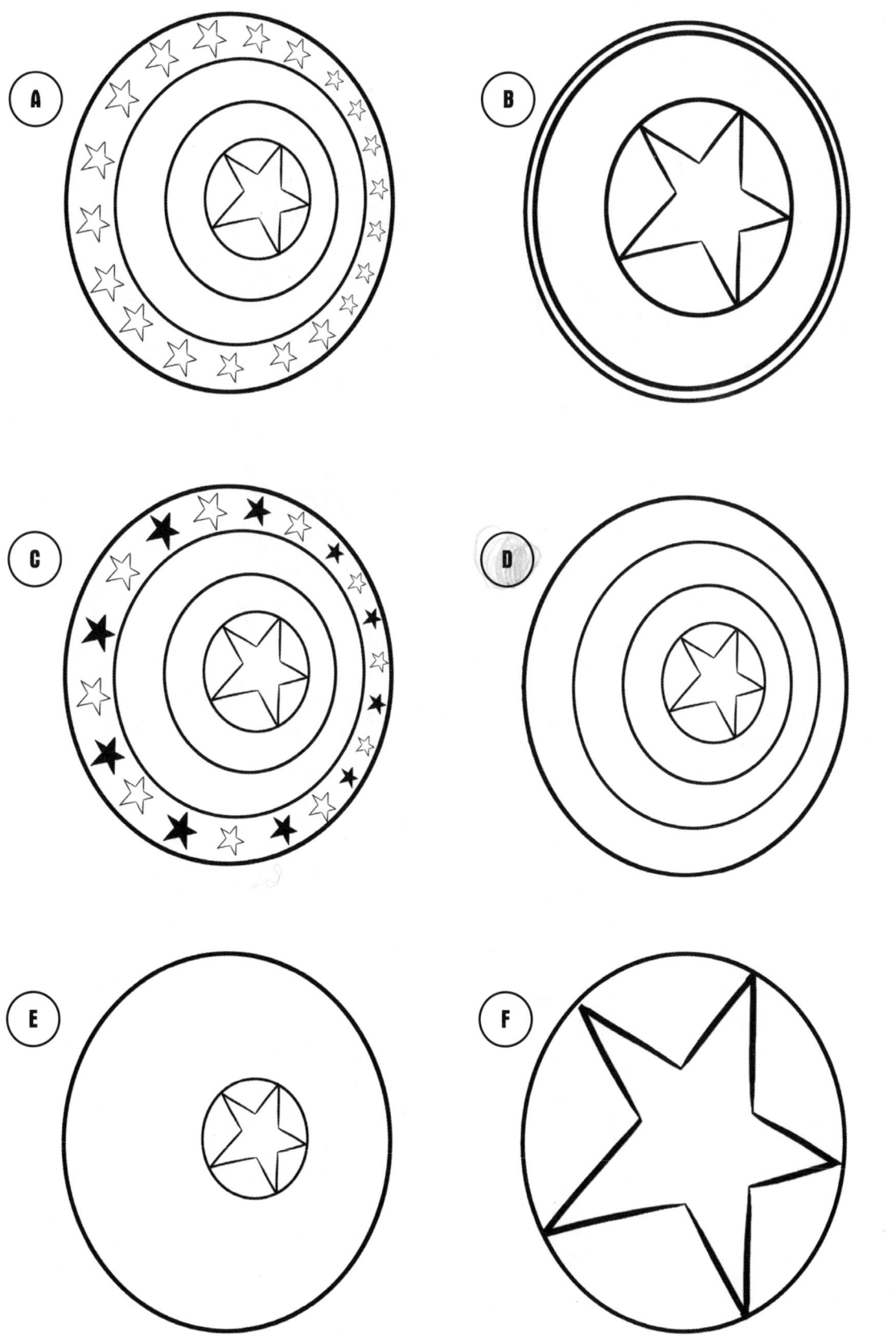

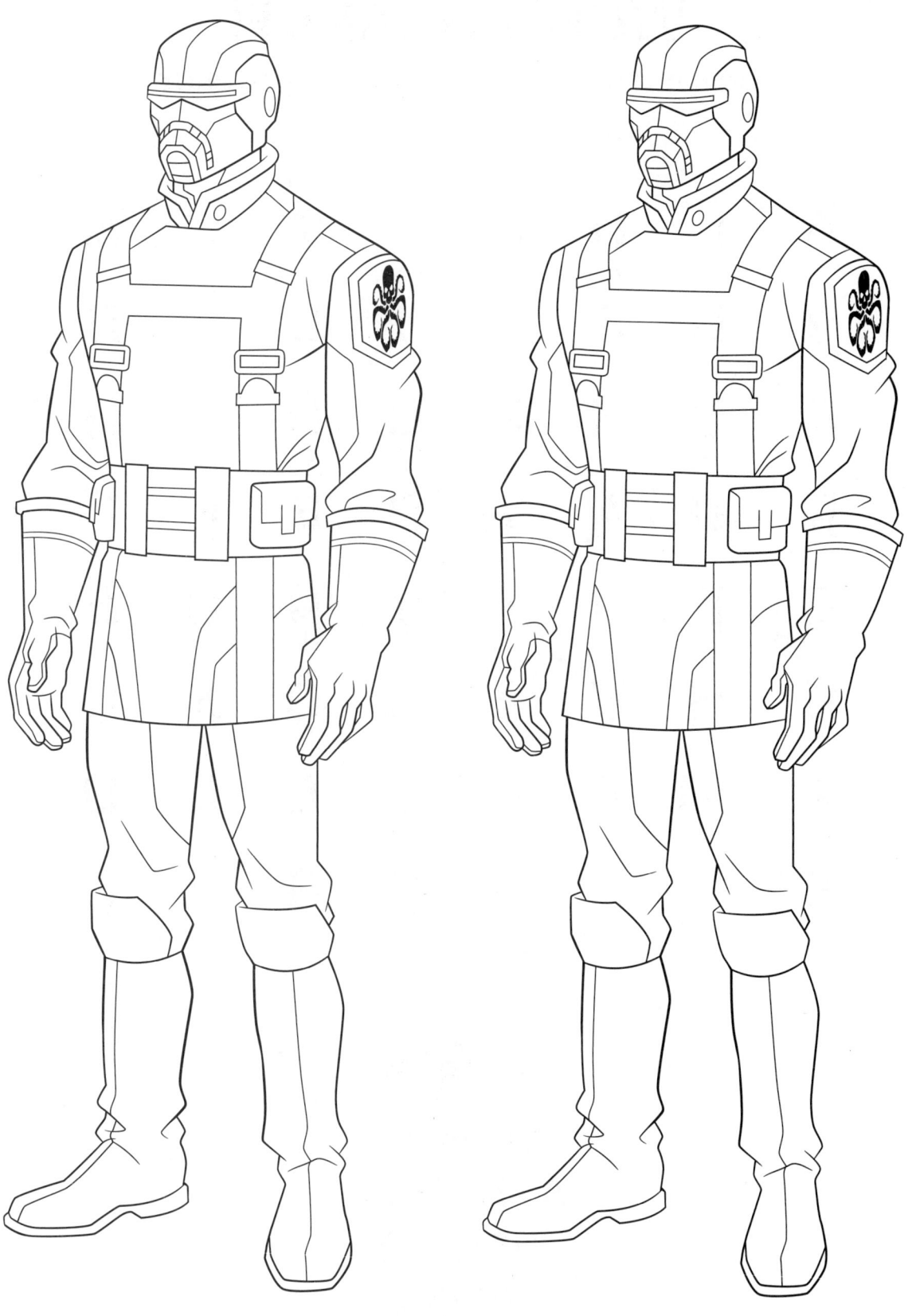

Hydra Agents fight with the Red Skull.

WORD SEARCH

How many of these words can you find?

A I U R T W H N
V D F H J E I S
E C H X U H I H
N D A W D E K I
G E R T V R U E
E H V E A O X L
R M A R V E L D
S I L P F S V E

★★★

MARVEL
AVENGERS
HEROES
SHIELD

★★★

GRID DRAWING

Draw Earth's newest Avenger: you!

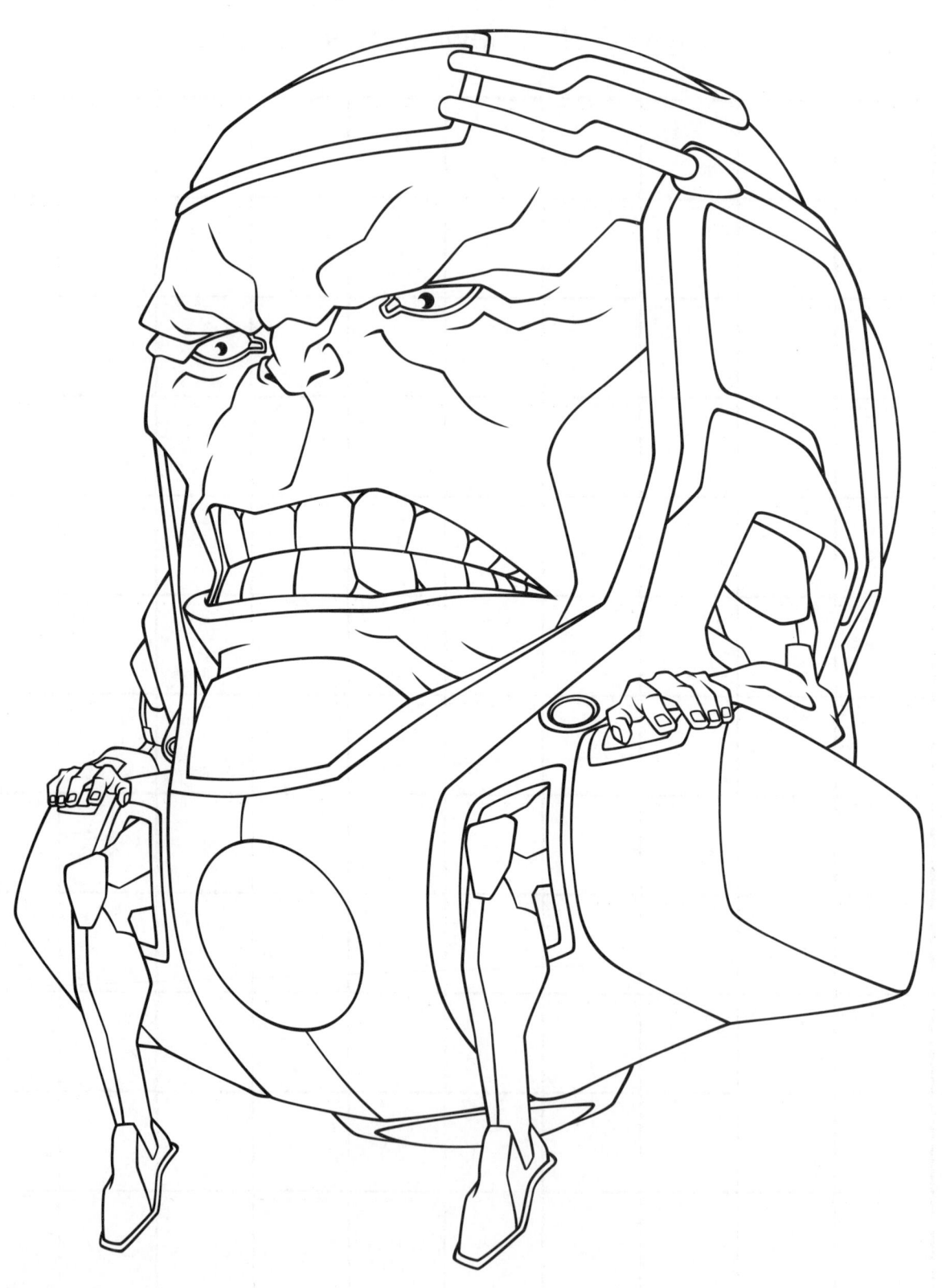

M.O.D.O.K. is the leader of A.I.M.

Project: Rebirth

SPOT THE DIFFERENCE

Look closely at the images below and see if
you can spot which M.O.D.O.K. is different.

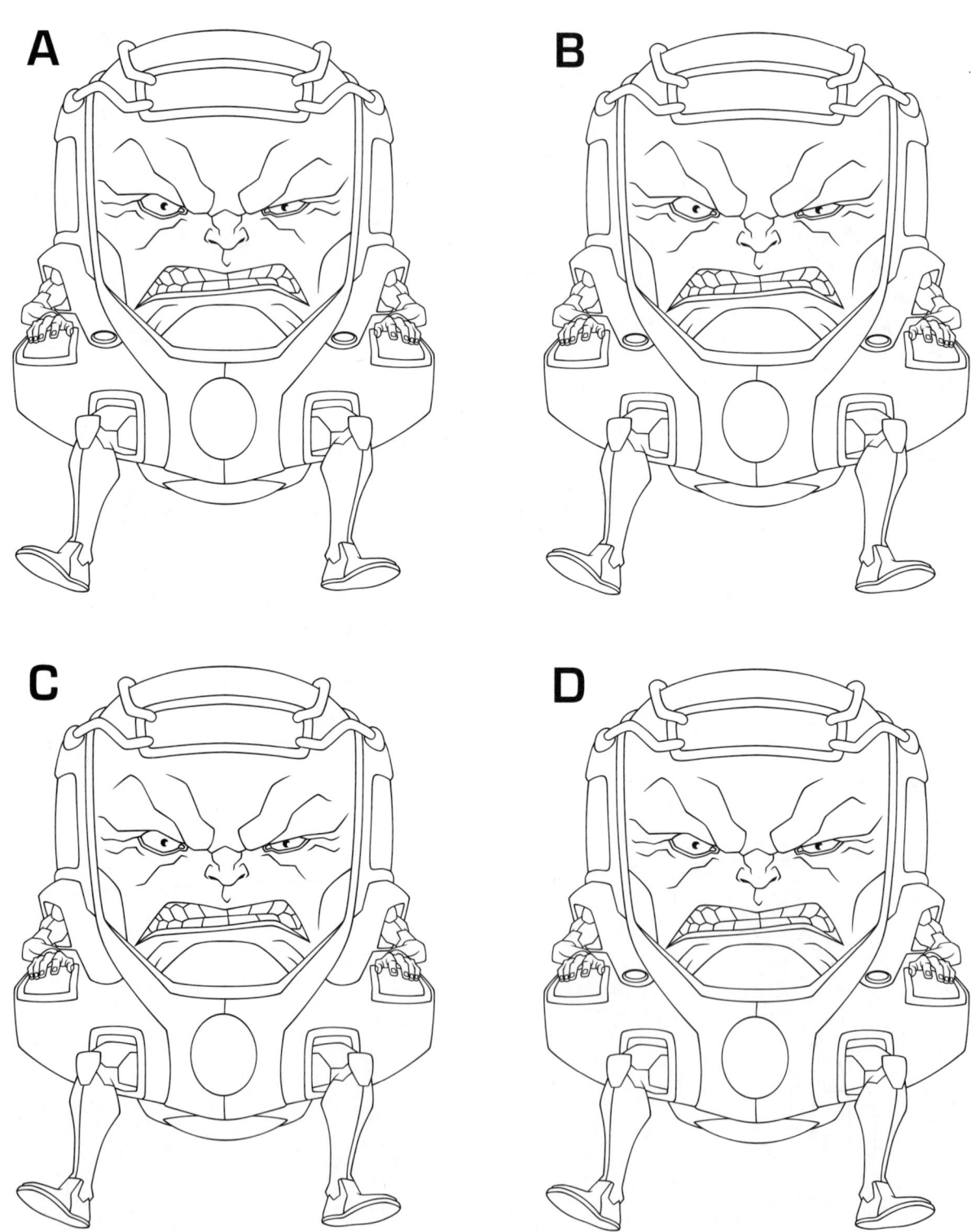

A

B

C

D

Reporting for duty!

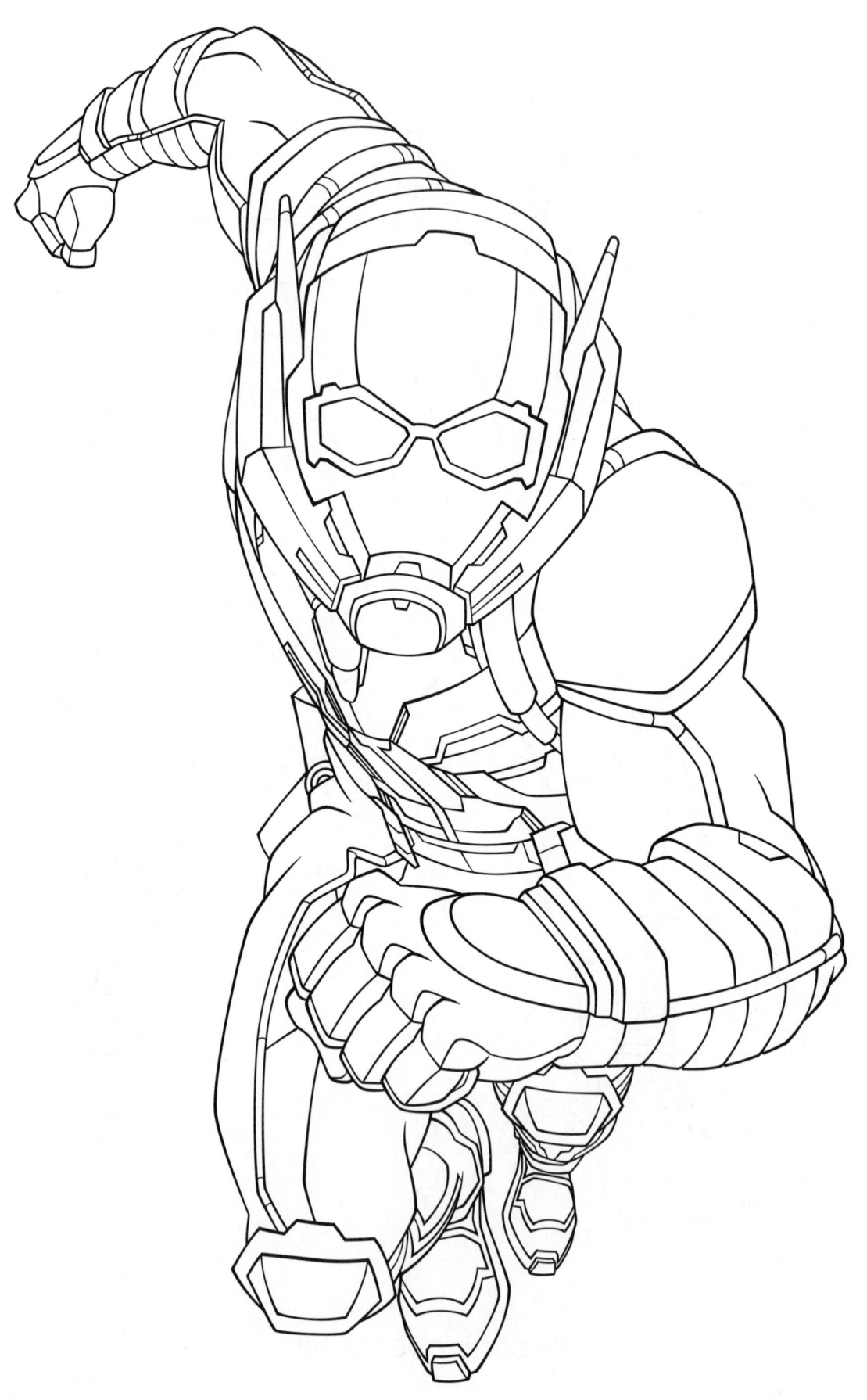

answer key

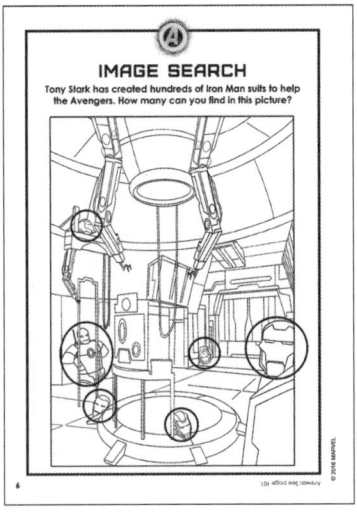

IMAGE SEARCH

Tony Stark has created hundreds of Iron Man suits to help the Avengers. How many can you find in this picture?

6

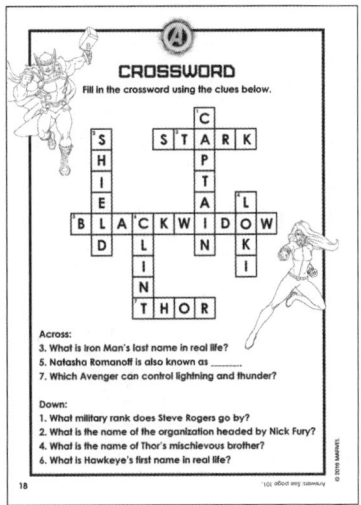

CROSSWORD

Fill in the crossword using the clues below.

```
              C
    S   S T A R K
    H   A
    I   P
    E   T
  B L A C K W I D O W
    D   A       O   L
        I       K   O
        N           K
        T H O R     I
```

Across:
3. What is Iron Man's last name in real life?
5. Natasha Romanoff is also known as _____
7. Which Avenger can control lightning and thunder?

Down:
1. What military rank does Steve Rogers go by?
2. What is the name of the organization headed by Nick Fury?
4. What is the name of Thor's mischievous brother?
6. What is Hawkeye's first name in real life?

18

MAZE

Thor needs to take the Bifröst Bridge from Asgard to Earth. Help Heimdall open the right path to get Thor there.

START

FINISH

20

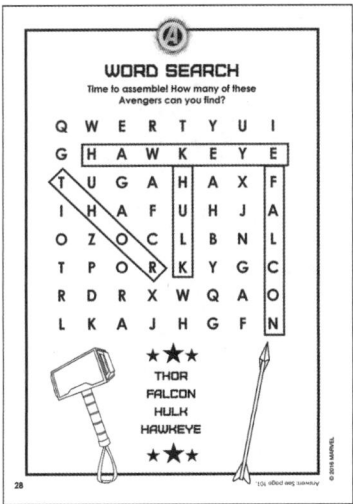

WORD SEARCH

Time to assemble! How many of these Avengers can you find?

```
Q W E R T Y U I
G H A W K E Y E
T U G A H A X F
I H A F U H J A
O Z O C L B N L
T P O R K Y G C
R D R X W Q A O
L K A J H G F N
```

★★★
THOR
FALCON
HULK
HAWKEYE
★★★

28

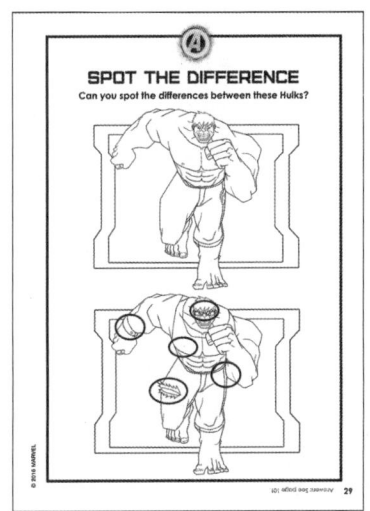

SPOT THE DIFFERENCE

Can you spot the differences between these Hulks?

29

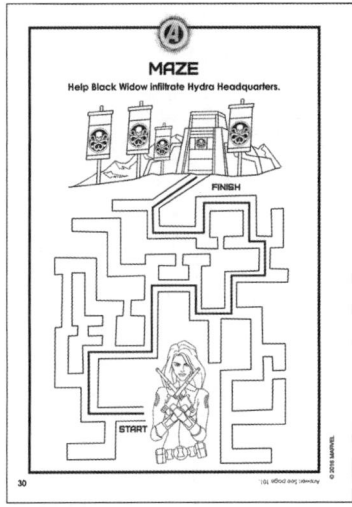

MAZE

Help Black Widow infiltrate Hydra Headquarters.

FINISH

START

30

MAZE

Nick Fury needs to assemble the Avengers team. Help each Avenger find the best path to the middle.

51

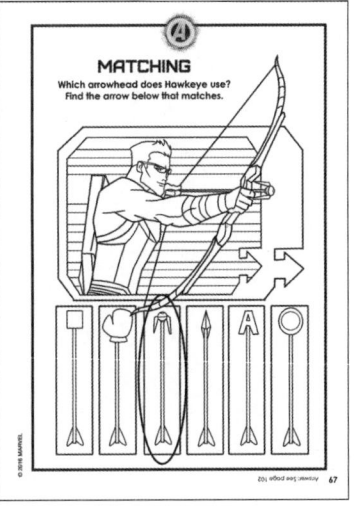

MATCHING

Which arrowhead does Hawkeye use? Find the arrow below that matches.

67

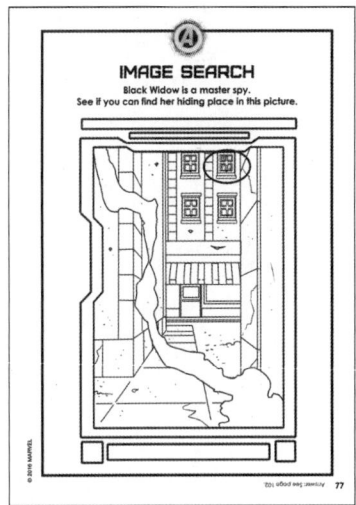

IMAGE SEARCH

Black Widow is a master spy. See if you can find her hiding place in this picture.

77

answer key

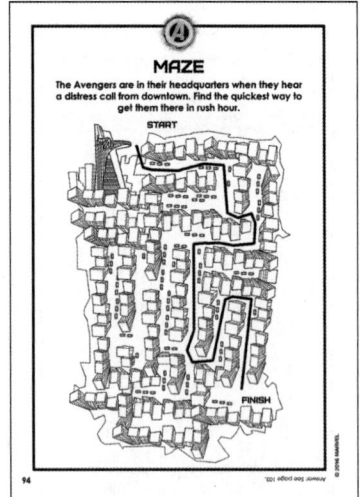

MAZE

The Avengers are in their headquarters when they hear a distress call from downtown. Find the quickest way to get them there in rush hour.

START

FINISH

94

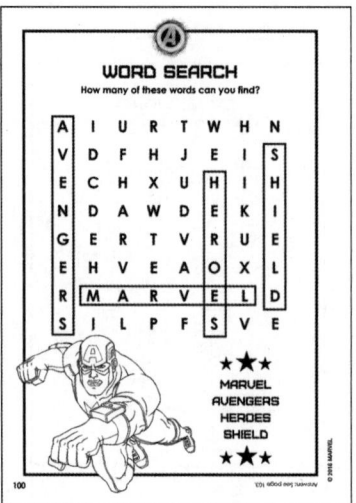

WORD SEARCH

How many of these words can you find?

A	I	U	R	T	W	H	N
V	D	F	H	J	E	I	S
E	C	H	X	U	H	I	H
N	D	A	W	D	E	K	I
G	E	R	T	V	R	U	E
E	H	V	E	A	O	X	L
R	M	A	R	V	E	L	D
S	I	L	P	F	S	V	E

★★★
MARVEL
AVENGERS
HEROES
SHIELD
★★★

100